TEST YOUR CHILD

Practical
Maths

Pat Milne

Headway · Hodder & Stoughton

Notes for parents and teachers

The value of practical work is being recognised more and more. Practical maths skills are of value in everyday life and can help with other school subjects. This booklet contains a range of topics for children aged 7–12. As well as questions and problems, it includes a number of practical tasks on:

Time, Money, Length, Weight, Shape, Area, Capacity and Volume.

The aim in using the booklet should be to encourage learning and build on feelings of success.

Schools vary in their approach to maths teaching and all children develop at different rates, so it is neither possible nor desirable to set the age by which a topic should have been covered.
Answers are given at the back, but it helps to remember that understanding is often more important than getting the right answer.

To gain maximum benefit, use the booklet as a *guide*, returning to it from time to time. It may reveal areas which cause problems, or, perhaps more important, which stimulate interest. The parent can help by encouraging follow-up work, using everyday settings and objects.

This Headway edition first published 1989
by Hodder and Stoughton Educational,
a division of Hodder and Stoughton Ltd,
Mill Road, Dunton Green, Sevenoaks, Kent

Third impression 1990

ISBN 0 340 50575 3

Printed and bound in Great Britain by CW Print Group, Loughton, Essex.

Time

1 How many days in a week? ....
2 How many months in a year? ....
3 Name the four seasons in the year ....
....

This shows part of the calendar for 1989

JANUARY

Monday		2	9	16	23	30
Tuesday		3	10	17	24	31
Wednesday		4	11	18	25	
Thursday		5	12	19	26	
Friday		6	13	20	27	
Saturday		7	14	21	28	
Sunday	1	8	15	22	29	

4 What month is it? ....
5 How many days in this month? ....
6 What day is the 10th? ....
7 What day is the 21st? ....
8 How many Mondays in this month? ....
9 What date is the second Tuesday? ....
10 What date is it a week earlier? ....
11 What month comes after this? ....
12 What month comes before this? ....
13 What date is the last Thursday? ....
14 What date is it a week later? ....

Write the times these clocks show

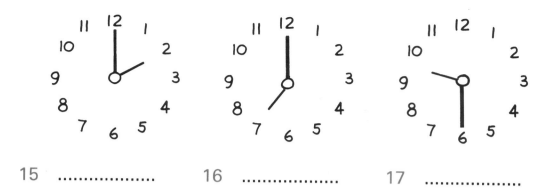

15 ....

16 ....

17 ....

18 How many minutes are in an hour? ....

19 How many hours in a day? ....

Make these clocks show the time below them

9 o'clock

20 minutes
past 2

40 minutes
past 7

This clock shows 6 o'clock. Write the time it will be

20 5 minutes later ....

21 25 minutes later ....

22 40 minutes later ....

23 1 hour later ....

This clock shows when John arrived home.

Ann arrived 35 minutes later. Show the time she arrived on this clock.

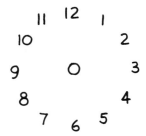

24 Write down the time she arrived. ....

....

Show these times on the clocks

[clock] 4.30

[clock] 8.40

[clock] 9.55

25–9 A train journey from Anntown to Bilby takes 25 minutes. Complete the timetable to show the arrival times.

Departure time from Anntown	6.00	7.10	9.30	10.35	11.50
Arrival time at Bilby					

Complete these times by writing am or pm

30 I get up at 7.30 ....

31 I start school at 9.00 ....

32 I have lunch at 12.45 ....

33 The milkman delivers at 7.00 ....

How long is it between

34 7 am and 11 am? ....

35 10 am and 2 pm? ....

36 Noon and 6.30 pm? ....

37 Midday and midnight? ....

38 2 pm and 1 am? ....

Write these times in a different way, as we would say them

39 5.05   .... past ....

40 9.40   .... to ....

41 How many weeks are there in a year? ....

42 How many days are there in a year? ....

43 How do you find the number of days in a particular number
    of weeks? ....

Find a calendar for this year. Using the calendar, write the full day and date for the following

The first Tuesday in May..

The fourth Thursday after the 1st July ....

The third day in September...

Two weeks after the 29th October ....

The day before the 1st January ....

Fill in the table to show the next 5 years and the day each year starts.

The next 5 years	19......	19......	19......	19......	19......
Day each year starts					

In what year will you be 21? ....

In what year will you be 58? ....

How many years till the year 2000? ....

What century will we be in then? ....

Write the following times in 24 hour clock notation

44   11 am ....

45   2.30 pm ....

46   12.30 pm ....

47   7.30 am ....

48   midday ....

49   $\frac{1}{4}$ to 6 at night ....

50   I am ....

51   10 past midnight ....

Complete the following table

	Departure time	Arrival time	Length of journey	
			HOURS	MINUTES
52	12.45	15.00		
53	14.10		2	35
54		23.58	2	42
55	23.40	02.10		
56	23.55		2	48
57		05.10	2	52

7

You will need a list of one day's television (from a newspaper or magazine). Choose one channel and look at the programmes.

Which channel did you select? ....

What is the longest programme? ....

How long does it last? ....

How long does the shortest programme last? ....

How much time is devoted to news? ....

What is the total viewing time possible? ....

What fraction of the viewing time, approximately, is devoted to news? ....

You need a device (a stopwatch or watch) for measuring in seconds. For each trial, write the letter 'A' 20 times and record the time it takes in seconds.

Example	A	A	A	A	A	A	A	A	A	A	A	A	A	A	A	A	A	A	A	A	Time in seconds
1st Trial																					
2nd Trial																					
3rd Trial																					

Total time

How long did it take altogether to do the three trials? ....

What is the average time of your three trials? ....

The last answer shows how long it took you on average to write how many 'A's? ....

Using this, how would you calculate your average time to write 'A' once? ....

Money

Draw and name the coins smaller than a 50p piece.
Find four different ways of making up 50p with the coins.

small cornet

20p

large cornet

30p

choc ice

25p

tub

35p

flake

15p

1 How much are a small cornet, a large cornet and a flake
   altogether? ....

2 What do three choc ices cost? ....

3 How many tubs can you buy for the cost of seven small
   cornets? ....

200p can be written as £2.00.
Write these the same way

4 100p .... 5 115p .... 6 80p .... 7 5p ....

8 £
   1.15
   + 2.30
   ———

   – – –

9 £
   1.92
   + 1.58
   ———

   – – –

10 £
    1.16
    – 0.95
    ———

    – – –

What change will I get from £3 if I spend

11 £1.50? .... 12 50p? .... 13 £1.08? ....

Calculate

14 £3.29 + £1.15 = ... 15 £2.80 – £1.22 = ...

9

16 £
   6.39
×   2
_____

_ _ _ _

17 £
   2.36
× 10
_____

_ _ _ _

18 £
   1.99
×   5
_____

_ _ _ _

19 Janet spent £3.75 on a bus fare and £2.55 on lunch.
How much did she spend altogether? ....

20 Brian had £5. He spent 95p on comics and 58p on sweets.
How much did he have left? ....

21 £

8)7.36

22 £

10)9.80

23 £

9)7.92

24 Ann has £7.92 and Bob has £20.00. How much more
has Bob than Ann? ....

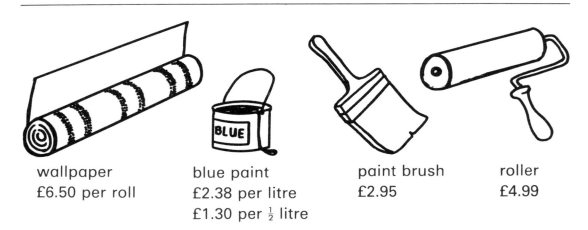

wallpaper	blue paint	paint brush	roller
£6.50 per roll	£2.38 per litre	£2.95	£4.99
	£1.30 per ½ litre		

Ruth's parents are decorating their bedroom. Find the cost of
the following which they need to buy.

25 8 rolls of wallpaper   cost = ...
26 2½ litres of blue paint   cost = ...
27 1 paint brush and 1 roller cost = ...
28 What is the total cost? ....

BIGBUS CO.	REDTOUR COMPANY	MOON COACHES
Adult £3.80	Adult £4.10	Child under 16 £2.30
Child under 14 £2.15	Child under 14 £2.05	Adult £4.25

The prices show the cost of a trip from Moonville to Nunstown by 3 bus companies.

29   Mr and Mrs Wells take their 3 children, all under 14, by Redtour Company. How much does it cost? ....

30   Mrs Black took her 4 children, aged 6, 8, 13 and 16 by Bigbus Co. How much did it cost? ....

Elaine aged 18 and Sue aged 15 did the journey twice one week by Moon Coaches.

31   How much did it cost altogether? ....

32   How much less did Sue pay than Elaine? ....

A teacher wants to take 10 children under 14 on the trip.

33   Which bus company will be cheapest? ....

34   If the children were all 15 years old which bus company would she be best to take? ....

35   A school can only buy pencils in boxes of 50, which cost £6 each. It needs to buy 1480 pencils. How much must it spend? ....

30 books cost £15.

36   What would 4 cost? ....

37   What would 72 cost? ....

38   5 oranges cost 49p. How much change will I get from £10 if I buy 20? ....

Length

Measure the length of your handspan in centimetres ....

How long do you think your foot is? ....

Draw its outline. Now measure it in centimetres.

How close was your estimate? ....

Measure the length of your bed in handspans ....

Now measure it in footlengths ....

Draw a table like this one.

	Estimate in cm	Length in cm
toothbrush this book pencil		

Gather together some objects and add them to the list.

Estimate, then measure the length of each *in cm.*

Keep doing this until you get really good at estimating.

1   How many centimetres are in a metre? ....

Using a tape measure to check the length, make your own metre rule. (You could use string or a piece of wood).

Draw a table like this one.

Just less than a metre	About one metre	Just more than a metre

Estimate the length of some things and fill in the table. (Try to find at least 5 things for each column).

Measure each with your metre rule to check your estimates.

Draw a table like this.

	Estimate	Length
length of bath height of door length of table height of chair		

Estimate the length of each as accurately as you can.
Now measure each and record your answer.
Try some other measurements and see how accurate your estimates can become.

___

2   A length of rope measures 1 m.   38 cm are cut off. What length is left? ....

3   Ann is 0.96 m tall. What height is this in centimetres? ....

___

Fill in the boxes

4   1 m [   ] cm ←→ *equals* ↓ 1.75 m ←→ *equals* ↓ [   ] cm

5   2 m   38   cm ←→ [m] ←→ [cm]

6   3 m   10   cm ←→ [m] ←→ [cm]

7   4 m   5   cm ←→ [m] ←→ [cm]

Draw a table like this.

Name	Estimate	Height

Estimate the height of members of your family.
You might ask a partner to make up another table of estimates.
Now measure and record their heights.
Check your measurements against those of your partner. Now
calculate the difference in height between each member.

You will need a ruler, string, and scissors.
Estimate, then measure, the lengths of each of the lines below.
(Record your results on a table like the previous ones.)

8    9 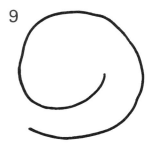   10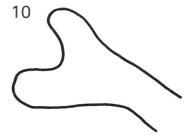

Draw longer lines on a large sheet of paper. Estimate, then
measure, each one.
Draw lines measuring:
a) 5 cm   b) 9 cm   c) 15 cm   d) $7\frac{1}{2}$ cm

---

11   A lawn is 9.85 m long and 7.65 m wide. What is the total
length of its edges? ....

12   The distance round a shape is called its:
(a) breadth   (b) perimeter   (c) area   (d) diagonal?

Estimate which of these has the largest perimeter.

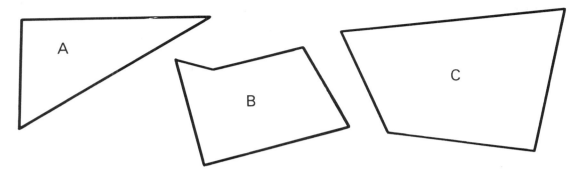

Now measure and record the perimeter of each shape.

13   A   14   B   15   C ....

___

16   A garage is 8 m long. It holds a car 4.80 m long and a trailer 2.15 m long. How much room is spare? ....

___

Measure lines A, B, C, D, E to the nearest millimetre.

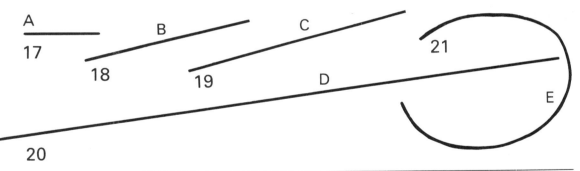

___

Complete these tables

	22	23	24	25	26	27
mm		30			1.8	
cm	1		40	2.8		562

	28	29	30	31	32	33
m		5000			600	
km	1		4.618	7.2		19

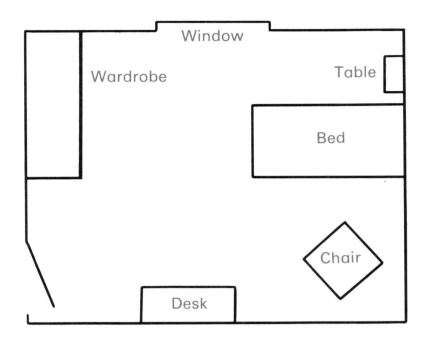

Plan of a bedroom

This plan is drawn to scale.

Measure the dimensions on the plan to fill in the table.

	actual	on plan
34 length of bed	200 cm	
35 length of window	150 cm	

Use the information from the table to find the *scale* used for the plan and complete the sentence

36 1 cm represents ....

Measure the dimensions of the desk and fill in this table.

	on plan	actual
37 length of desk		
38 width of desk		

39 What is the *actual* area of the desk top? .... cm²

40 Is this more or less than 1m²? ....

16

Weight

You will need kitchen scales.

Select 5 packets or tins of food.

Do not look at the weight marked on the labels.

Balance each one in your hand. Arrange them in order of weight.

LIGHTEST ←————————————————————→ HEAVIEST

....

Draw a table like this one. Estimate the weight of each of your 5 objects.

Name of object	Estimate	Weight

Now weigh each one in grams.

1 A cup weighs 150 g and a saucer weighs 198 g. What is the total weight? ....

2 A sock weighs 118 g. What would a pair weigh?...................

You need 2 books. Estimate then weigh each book.

	Estimate	Weight
Book 1		
Book 2		
Total:		

Add the two weights to find the total weight

Now weigh the two books together. Do you get the same answer?

3 How many grams in a kilogram? ....

4 How many grams in $\frac{3}{4}$ kilogram? ....

A recipe for fruit cake requires

250 g plain flour   900 g mixed fruit
300 g self-raising flour   10 eggs
450 g butter   1 tablespoon treacle
450 g sugar   1 tablespoon syrup

5 What is the total weight of flour needed? ....

6 How much more self-raising than plain flour is needed?

   ....

What is the total weight of dry ingredients

7 for 1 cake? ....

8 for 3 cakes? ....

9 How many cakes could you make from 1 kg butter? ....

Fill in the boxes.

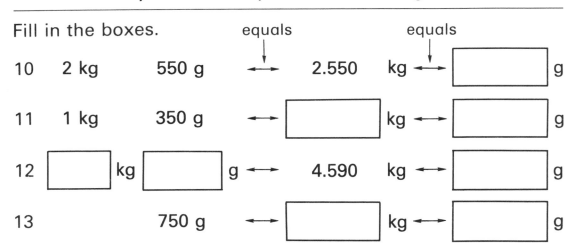

			equals			equals	
10	2 kg	550 g	←→	2.550	kg	←→ [ ]	g
11	1 kg	350 g	←→ [ ]	kg	←→ [ ]	g
12	[ ] kg	[ ] g	←→	4.590	kg	←→ [ ]	g
13		750 g	←→ [ ]	kg	←→ [ ]	g

What weight will balance the scales?

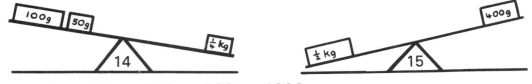

14 50 g, 100 g, 200 g, 500 g, 1000 g ....

15 50 g, 100 g, 200 g, 500 g, 1000 g ....

16 Which is the same as 5000 g?
    50 kg, 500 kg, 5000 kg, 5 kg, 0.5 kg   ....

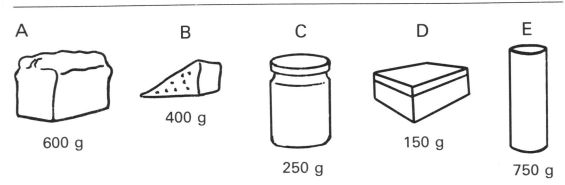

A 600 g   B 400 g   C 250 g   D 150 g   E 750 g

Which of these could be put together to make up a parcel weighing

17 800 g? ....

18 1.5 kg? ....

19 Bill and Ben stand on a weighing machine. It registers 68.58 kg. When Bill steps off the weight drops to 32.92 kg. How heavy is Bill? ....

Cat litter costs 45p per kg

20 How heavy is a bag costing £3.15? ....

21 What is the cost of a bag weighing 4.2 kg? ....

22 Which is the same as 75 g?
    0.75 kg, 0.075 kg, 75000 kg, 7500 kg, 0.0075 kg

    ....

23 Which is the same as 0.42 kg?
    42 g, 4.2 g, 0.42 g, 420 g, 4200 g ....

24 120 kg of flour is put in 2 sacks so that one is three times heavier than the other. What is the difference in weight between the 2 sacks? ....

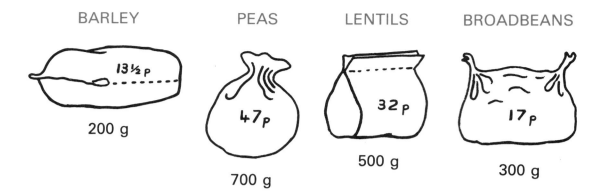

BARLEY

13½ p

200 g

PEAS

47 p

700 g

LENTILS

32 p

500 g

BROADBEANS

17 p

300 g

25 If you wanted 1 kg of dried vegetables, which kind would be
the cheapest? ....

Use kitchen scales and select 5 objects.
Measure and record the weight of each
(a) to the nearest kg
(b) to the nearest ½ kg
(c) to the nearest 100 g
(d) to the nearest 50 g
(e) to the nearest 10 g

Shape

Fill in the table to show how many squares you can count in each diagram.

Do the same for rectangles and triangles.

P 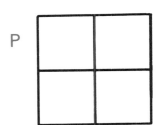   Q 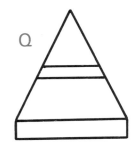   R

	Squares	Rectangles	Triangles
1 P			
2 Q			
3 R			

4   How many right angles are there in P? ....

How many right angles can you find in the room you are in?

Find a cuboid

5   How many faces has it? ....

6   How many edges? ....

7   A cube is a special kind of cuboid. What makes it special? ....

8   How many sides has a hexagon? ....   Draw one.

You need paper and scissors.
Fold the paper in half.

Draw an outline of half a butterfly.

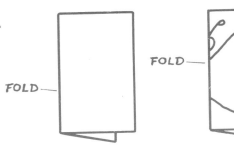

Cut round the outline you have drawn.

Open up your picture.

Draw in the line of symmetry.

Colour your drawing. Try to make it as symmetrical as possible.

Make some more symmetrical shapes.

9   List the letters of the alphabet which have line symmetry.

Make a list of some symmetrical words.

Draw a shape like this using squares of side 1 cm.

A net of a cube

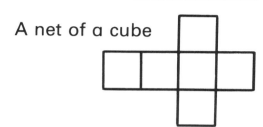

Cut out your shape.

Fold it up to make a cube.

Now draw and cut out 2 more nets for a cube of side 1 cm.

Make sure they are different to this one.

Find the size of angles, A, B and C, in degrees. Label each 'obtuse' or 'acute'.

10   A   11   B   12   C ....

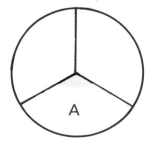
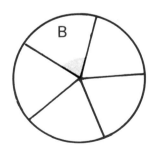
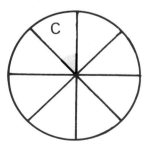

Use a coloured pencil to join up the ends of the spikes in each circle. Write down the name of the shape you have made in each case.

13   A   14   B   15   C ....

Draw round the base of a cylindrical object to make a circle. Cut it out. By folding it twice find its centre.

You need a pair of compasses.
Draw a circle with radius O P.

O ——————— P

16 How long is its diameter? ....

Now draw one with radius 35 mm.

17 Which has the larger area? ....

Find a way of measuring the circumference of a 10p piece.

_____

You will need a protractor.
Construct an angle of 50°.

18 This angle should measure 130°.
    Is it accurate? ....

Draw an obtuse angle less than 100°.

Estimate which angle below is nearest to 118°.
Measure each angle.

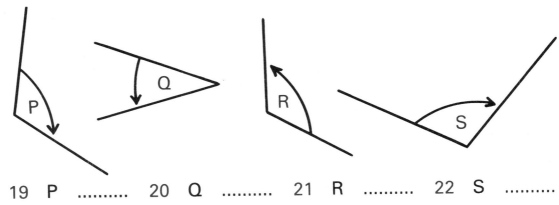

19 P .... 20 Q .... 21 R .... 22 S ....

Area

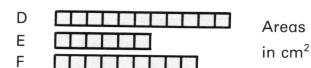

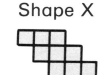
Shape X

Areas
in cm²

1   Which bar has an area the same as shape X? ....
Draw another rectangle which has the same area as E.

2   Which of the shapes below have the same area? ....

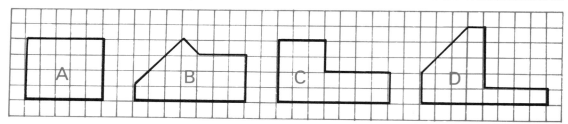

Draw 4 shapes each with an area of 24 squares.
Draw 3 rectangles each with an area of 12 cm².

This shape has a perimeter of 12 cm
and an area of 6 cm².
Find as many different shapes
as you can with perimeter 12 cm
and area 6 cm².
Draw sketches on squared paper
to show them.

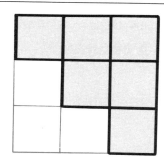

3   What is the area of this
    triangle in cm² ?

Draw a right-angled
triangle with area 15 cm².
Draw a trapezium with an
area of 12 cm².
Draw a parallelogram with an area of 12 cm².

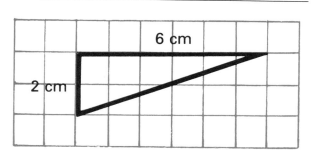

4 Find the area of this rhombus,
   in squares, in two different ways.

Find the area of each rectangle

5 A ....

6 B ....

7 C ....

A

1.5 cm

2.4 cm

B

2½ cm

1½ cm

C

30 mm

11 mm

8 Which has the smallest area? ....

Find the area of each triangle

9 D ....   10 E ....   11 F ....

D

2 cm

2 cm

E

1½ cm

4 cm

F

3.5 cm

1½ cm

12 Which has the greatest area? ....

Find the areas represented by the following plans

13 P ....   14 Q ....   15 R ....

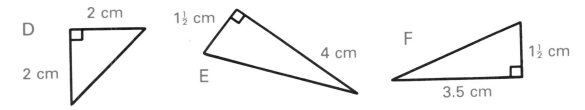

P

1.8 cm

2 cm   2 cm

Q

2 m   1 m   3 m

2½ m   2½ m

R

2 km   1 km   4 km   1 km

Complete the table to show 6 rectangles each with an area of 12 cm².

Rectangle	A	B	C	D	E	F
Length of first side (cm)	12		4		2	
Length of second side (cm)	1			4		

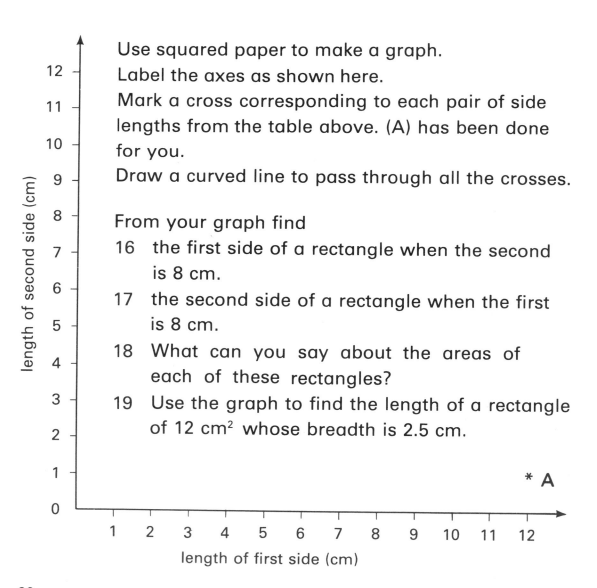

Use squared paper to make a graph.
Label the axes as shown here.
Mark a cross corresponding to each pair of side lengths from the table above. (A) has been done for you.
Draw a curved line to pass through all the crosses.

From your graph find

16   the first side of a rectangle when the second is 8 cm.

17   the second side of a rectangle when the first is 8 cm.

18   What can you say about the areas of each of these rectangles?

19   Use the graph to find the length of a rectangle of 12 cm² whose breadth is 2.5 cm.

Capacity and volume

Using a litre bottle of water how many times could you fill a glass which holds

1 $\frac{1}{2}$ litre? ....

2 $\frac{1}{4}$ litre? ....

3 $\frac{1}{10}$ litre? ....

You will need a litre bottle (for example, an empty lemonade bottle).

Find a container you think holds $\frac{1}{2}$ l.

Find another one you think holds $\frac{1}{4}$ l.

Find a third you think holds $\frac{1}{10}$ l.

Fill your litre bottle with water.

How many times can you fill the first container? Record your answer on the table.

Do the same for the other two containers.

From your answers, complete the sentences by writing 'more' or 'less'.

Container	No of times you can fill it	Does each hold 'more' or 'less' than your estimate?	Vol in ml
1 2 3		holds ....than $\frac{1}{2}$ l holds ....than $\frac{1}{4}$ l holds ....than $\frac{1}{10}$ l	

If you have a jug with a marked scale, find the volume of water each container can hold, in millilitres, as accurately as you can. Record this on the table.

Complete the table

4	5	6	7	8	9	10
2 litres	$\frac{1}{2}$ litre	0.75 litre	$\frac{1}{10}$ litre	l	l	l
ml	ml	ml	ml	3500 ml	465 ml	50 ml

11 A pot of jam holding $1\frac{1}{2}$ l fills 6 jam jars of equal size. How much does each jar hold in millilitres? ....

12 This table shows the prices of 5 tubes of handcream. Which is best value for money? ....

Tube	A	B	C	D	E
Volume	$\frac{1}{2}$ l	150 ml	200 ml	$\frac{1}{4}$ l	120 ml
Price	£1.55	48p	56p	75p	42p

From your local shop find the volume and price for 4 different shampoos. Record your findings on a table. Calculate which type gives you best value for money.

You will need a measuring jug (with a scale marked on) and 4 small objects (A, B, C and D).
Estimate the volume of each object in ml. Record your estimates in column 2 of the table on the next page.
Now follow these steps to find the volume of each object.
(a) Pour water into the jug. Record the volume in column 3.
(b) Immerse one object in the water. Record the new level of water in column 4.

(c) Use columns 3 and 4 to calculate the volume of each object
for column 5.

	1 Name of object	2 Estimate of Volume	3 Volume of water	4 Volume of water and object	5 Volume of object
A					
B					
C					
D					

Write out your objects in order of volume.

SMALLEST ◄.............. ....► LARGEST

Weigh each object and write out in order of weight
LIGHTEST ◄.............. ....►HEAVIEST

Is the order the same for volume and weight?
Does weight always depend on volume?
Can you think of something large and light?
Can you think of something small and heavy?

_____

You will need 3 strong boxes (cuboid or cube shaped).
Find the volume of each in two ways
(a) by measuring length, width and height and then multiplying
    ($l \times w \times h$ = volume)
(b) by measuring the volume of water or sand you need to fill
    each one.

Complete the following

13 1 cm³ is equivalent in volume to [ ] ml.

14 1 litre is equivalent in volume to [ ] cm³.

15 ¼ litre is equivalent in volume to [ ] cm³.

16 300 cm³ is equivalent in volume to [ ] ml.

17 500 ml is equivalent in volume to [ ] ....

18 How many litres of water can a rectangular tank hold which is 40 cm long, 20 cm wide and 30 cm high?

19 A rectangular tank holds 200 litres of water. If the tank is 5 m long and 2 m wide, how high is the water in the tank? ....

20 A cube shaped milk tank can hold 8 litres. Milk is poured in to a height of 10 cm. How much more milk can be added? Answer in litres ....

Answers

Time
(Where times are asked for in this section, any form of the correct answer, e.g. 9.30, nine thirty, half past nine, is acceptable.)
1. 7 2. 12 3. Spring, Summer, Autumn, Winter 4. January 5. 31 6. Tuesday
7. Saturday 8. 5 9. 10th 10. 3rd 11. February 12. December 13. 26th
14. 2nd February 15. two o'clock 16. seven o'clock 17. half past nine 18. 60 19. 24
20. 6.05 21. 6.25 22. 6.40 23. 7 o'clock 24. 4.30 25. 6.25 26. 7.35 27. 9.55
28. 11.00 29. 12.15 30. am 31. am 32. pm 33. am 34. 4 hours 35. 4 hours
36. 6½ hours 37. 12 hours 38. 11 hours 39. five past five 40. twenty to ten
41. 52 42. 365 43. multiply the weeks by seven 44. 11.00 45. 14.30 46. 12.30
47. 07.30 48. 12.00 49. 17.45 50. 01.00 51. 00.10 52. 2 h 15 min 53. 16.45
54. 21.16 55. 2 h 30 min 56. 02.43 57. 02.18

Money
1. 65p 2. 75p 3. 4 4. £1.00 5. £1.15 6. £0.80 7. £0.05 8. £3.45 9. £3.50
10. £0.21 11. £1.50 12. £2.50 13. £1.92 14. £4.44 15. £1.58 16. £12.78
17. £23.60 18. £9.95 19. £6.30 20. £3.47 21. 92p 22. 98p 23. 88p 24. £12.08
25. £52 26. £6.06 27. £7.94 28. £66.00 29. £14.35 30. £14.05 31. £13.10
32. £3.90 33. Redtour 34. Moon Coaches 35. £180 36. £2.00 37. £36.00 38. £8.04

Length
1. 100 2. 62 cm 3. 96 cm 4. 75/175 cm 5. 2.38 m/238 cm 6. 310 m/310 cm
7. 4.05 m/405 cm 8. 5 cm 9. 13 cm 10. 12 cm 11. 35 m 12. (b) 13. 14 14. 13
15. 17 16. 1.05 m 17. 20 mm 18. 45 mm 19. 60 mm 20. 154 mm 21. 110 m
22. 10 mm 23. 3 cm 24. 400 mm 25. 28 mm 26. 0.18 cm 27. 5620 mm 28. 1000 m
29. 5 km 30. 4618 m 31. 7200 m 32. 0.6 km 33. 19,000 m 34. 4 cm 35. 3 cm
36. 50 cm 37. 2.5 cm, 125 cm 38. 1 cm, 50 cm 39. 6250 cm² 40. less

Weight
1. 348 g 2. 236 g 3. 1000 g 4. 750 g 5. 550 g 6. 50 g 7. 2.35 kg (2350 g) 8. 7.05 kg
(7050 g) 9. 2 10. 2550 g 11. 1.35 kg/1350 g 12. 4 kg 590 g/4590 g 13. 0.75 kg/750 g
14. 100 g 15. 100 g 16. 5 kg 17. B, C, D 18. A, D, E 19. 35.66 kg 20. 7 kg 21. £1.89
22. 0.075 kg 23. 420 g 24. 60 kg 25. Broadbeans

Shape
1. 5/4/0 2. 0/1/3 3. 3/2/6 4. 16 5. 6 6. 12 7. All the sides are equal length 8. 6
9. ABCDEHIKMOTUVWXYZcovwx 10. 120° obtuse 11. 72° acute 12. 45° acute
13. Triangle 14. Pentagon 15. Octagon 16. 8 cm 17. the first 18. No. It measures
140° 19. 117° (nearest 118°) 20. 35° 21. 120° 22. 105°

Area

1. F 2. A, B and C 3. 12 cm² 4. 8 cm² 5. 3.6 cm² 6. 3¾ or 3.75 cm² 7. 330 mm² 8. C 9. 2 cm² 10. 3 cm² 11. 2.625 cm² 12. E 13. 3.6 cm² 14. 8.75 m² 15. 6 km² 16. 1.5 cm 17. 1.5 cm 18. They are equal 19. 4.8 cm

Capacity and Volume

1. twice 2. four times 3. ten times 4. 2000 ml 5. 500 ml 6. 750 ml 7. 100 ml 8. 3.5 l 9. 0.465 l 10. 0.05 l 11. 250 ml 12. C 13. 1 14. 1000 15. 250 16. 300 17. 500 cm³ or 0.5 l 18. 24 l 19. 2 m 20. 4 l